TEXTUAL NOTES

Composition Mannheim, Oct–Nov 1777

Sources autograph lost; an MS copy by Leopold Mozart (to whom Mozart sent his own MS shortly after the sonata's composition) survives in a Swiss private collection and a photocopy has kindly been made available by the Neue Mozart-Ausgabe [L]; the first edition is as no.1 of *Trois sonates pour le clavecin ou le forte piano* (Paris: Heina, 1782) (nos.2 and 3 are K310/300*d* and K311/284*c*) [E]; and two copies in Stift Melk, Austria, have also been consulted, by kind permission of the librarian, the earlier being no.1 in a set 'Sechs Sonaten' [M1], the later 'Sonata in C per il clavi cembalo o forte piano' [M2]

Notes M1 has much additional slurring, not shown here, and some additional dynamic marks, some of which are included here editorially where justified by analogy with L or E

1st movt E gives tempo as 'Allegro con spiritoso'

bar	
13–14	L, slurs possibly *1–4*
15–19, 110–14	alternate *p* and *f* not in L; in E only 113–14; M1 has as shown in 15–19 except *p* in 16 (that and *p–f–p* in 110–11 editorial by analogy with 113–14)
21–6, 116–22	M1 gives *fp* on 1st note of each 2-bar phrase, *cresc.* later in bar (not 23)
23,25	arpeggiation from E
24	stacc. from E.
27	M1, *f* on *1*, *sf* on *c'''* (also 28)
33–4	LH dynamics not in E
38,41	RH, 3rd slur from E
42	LH *f* in M1 only, though implied by stacc. wedges in L; RH slurs from E
43	*f* from E
48–9, 142–3	dynamics reversed in E
58	arpeggiation from E
63	*p* from E
74–8	slurs not in E
80–1	stacc. from E, 80, final note, 81, *1–4*
89	E has *p* for *pp*
91	slurs from E
98	LH, 2nd slur from E
103	E, RH *6*♮ for ♭; *p* from E
106	L, LH ♮ for ♭ to *a*
112	L, LH *3 d*
120	arpeggiation from E
124	M1, LH, crotchet *g–g'* 1st beat, q rest, then as other sources
128	*f* not in E
129	LH *p* not in E
131	LH, 3rd slur from E
136	LH *f* as 42

2nd movt E slurring less careful and less complete than L; divergences in E not detailed unless they supply a deficiency in L or might represent valid alternative readings

bar	
6	L no slur 1st beat; E, slur *1–3*: cf. 5, 49
8	L slur *1–3*, none in E; L, RH *e'* missing
10	L, LH 2nd *c'* missing
13	L slur ?*2–4*
17–18	L has only *f*; E has *fp* (RH), *f* (LH) in 17, *fp* (LH) in 18
22	*f* in E
27	LH 2nd slur from
30–1	E, RH slurs over dsqs
32	LH slur and tie from E
33	RH 2nd slur from E
36	RH slur from E
38	E, RH last note *b''*♭ (a possible reading)
54	RH 2nd slur from E
61	*f''* not ♯ in L (but ♮ in 62 implies accidental omission)
63	L, *g'* marked ♯ in error; last 2 slurs from E
65	RH last slur from E
67	E (also M1 and M2), *d'* for *f'*
73	L, LH slur *1–3*; none in E
76	RH 1st slur from E
77	*pp* from E
78	E, RH *e* lacking

3rd movt E: 'Rondau Allegretto gratioso'

bar	
1	*p* from E; LH slurring in 4s (also 93ff, 116ff) by analogy with L, 189–93 and E, 189, 194; RH slurs by analogy with E, 93–8
1,3,11	stacc. by analogy with L, 95, 195; also 93, 99, 189, 191
19	*f* from E
32	L, RH articulation lacking in 2nd half of bar
42	slur from E
43	*f* from E
54	L, LH last *f'*♯ lacking
66	*p* from E
68	slur from E
71	some edns give LH 1st chord *g–b*♭, but L and E agree *b*♮; the same applies to 175 (*e*♭/♮) and 226 (*f*♮/♯)
76	L, 2nd chord, *d''* lacking
77–82	sources ambiguous about dot/wedge stacc.; also 210–18
85	E, LH last 3 qs slurred; *f* from E
93ff	see 1
108–9	E has RH only *3* and *4* stacc., slurs *5–8*
110	E has RH slurs *5–6*, *7–8*, last one lacking in LH
115	E, RH *2 b''*♭
117,121	LH altered in later edns to give dominant harmony on 1st beat; text here as in L and E
119	LH, L has ♭ to *3* and *6*, and *7* is *a'*; E has ♮ to *3*, ♭ to *6*, and *7* is *g'*
124, 127–8	LH altered in later edns, 1st beat of 124 and 128, last of 127; text here as in L and E
127	2nd slur from E
132–6	articulation from E in 133; E lacks slurs 132, 134, 136
162	L 1st chord *c–c'*; *e–c'*, as in E, clearly correct
167	L, top note of LH chord *c*; E gives *d*; cf. 67
189ff	see 1
201	L, *c'''* for *e'''*
217–18	no stacc. in E
226	see 71
228	*p* from E
230–1	RH top note *e'''* in L, E and M2 (with no ♮ in 232 to suggest an omission); M1 and some later edns give the harmonically more probable *e'''*♭
236	L, LH *E* and *C* lacking
240	L, LH last chord *g–b–d'*; text follows E and analogy with 241
245ff	E, LH articulation lacking

SONATA in C

K309/284*b* (1777)

Allegro con spirito

* The alternate *f*-*p* here and in bars 110-11 should be regarded as optional: see Textual Notes.

5
crescendo
or
A.B.1560

p
f
p
f
p
pp
cresc.
cresc.
f
p
f
f
p
f
p
f
p
tr
tr

p
crescendo f
p
p
Practise emphasis on 2,4,6,8.
lift
lift
lift
f
f

Andante un poco adagio
cresc.

fp
p
f
tr
cresc.
pp
fp
f
fp
p

f
p
cresc.
fp
tr

RONDEAU
Allegretto grazioso

42
48
50
54
cresc.
58

or
61
65
70
73
76

f
p
tr

p
f
f
p
fp
p
fp
f
fp
fp
f
tr

cresc.
cresc.

or
etc.
or
etc.
tr
cresc.

✱ see **Textual Notes**

A|B|R|S|M
PUBLISHING

The Associated Board of the Royal Schools of Music (Publishing) Limited

14 Bedford Square
London WC1B 3JG

ISBN 1-85472-124-0